Lucky

Poems and Drawings by
ROGER McGOUGH

F
FRANCES LINCOLN
CHILDREN'S BOOKS

Contents

My Pet Stoat

My favourite pet
is a baby stoat
With bright blue eyes
and a tortoiseshell coat

Warm and cuddly
he curls up on my lap
Or in front of the fire
while taking a nap

On the back of a chair
he'll balance and spring
Then play for hours
with a ball of string

When I stroke his back
it's as soft as silk
And he goes 'Miaow'
when its time for his milk

Excuse me, that's not a stoat

No?

No, *that's a cat.*

It's not a cat. I've got a cat. I keep it in a little cage hanging from the mantelpiece.

A cat in a cage? What does it look like?

It's got wires going this way and that way...

No. I mean the cat.

Just like any other cat, I suppose. It's got a little beak, covered in feathers and goes, 'Tweet Tweet.'

Tweet Tweet?

Tweet Tweet.

That's not a cat.

No?

No, that's a canary.

It's not a canary. I've got a canary. I keep it in the kennel in the backyard.

A canary in a kennel? What does it look like?

It's a wooden box with a roof…

No, I mean the canary.

Just like any other canary. It's huge, grey, with huge floppy ears, two tusks and a big long trunk.

That's not a canary.

No? What is it, then?

It's … er … why, everybody knows,
It's… er … you know … it's … a … GOLDFISH!

No Peas for the Wicked

No peas for the wicked
No carrots for the damned
No parsnips for the naughty
O Lord we pray

No beansprouts for the bad-tempered
No noodles for the moody
No onions for the whingers
No way, no way

No garlic for the greedy
No beetroot for the bullies
No mange-tout for the muggers
Lock them away

No broccoli for the smelly
No cabbage for the cheeky
No corn for the fare-dodgers
Make 'em all pay

No creamy mash or aubergines
No fries, no baked or refried beans
No vegetables of any kind
O Lord we pray

A Weasel is Easily Pleased

A weasel is easily pleased
just give him biscuits and crumbly cheese
tickle his whiskers
and if there's a breeze
invite him sailing
and if he agrees
it's anchors aweigh
on the open seas.

A weasel is easily pleased
and when the snow
begins to freeze
take him skiing
on the Pyrenees
down the slopes
in and·out of the trees
'Look out everybody
a weasel on skis!'

A weasel is easily pleased
just give him an easel
and soon he'll be seized
with a passion for painting
still-lives of peas.
Carrots, parsnips
veggies like these
the occasional onion
but mainly, peas.

Class Warfare

I'm the most important
Person in the class
Twenty-four-carat diamond
While all the rest are glass

Distinctions distinguish me
While others strive to pass
I'm en route for glory
While others are en masse

They're backdrops, they're bit parts
They're day-old candy floss
They provide the undercoat
For my enduring gloss

They're small fry, they're chiff chaff
Insignificant and dross
I'm in a league of my own
The undisputed boss.

When I go down in history
I'll go down a storm
For I'm the most important
Person in the form

(If you don't believe me
Ask Daddy – he's the headmaster.)

A Meerkat Lullaby

Hush pretty meerkitten don't you cry
Mummy will sing you a lullaby
Daddy on guard, is standing near
Ready to bark should danger appear.

His back is straight, his hindlegs long
His hearing acute, his eyesight strong
So go to sleep my little beauty
Safe with Daddy on sentry duty.

Wasps

useless things

short-tempered, whining

stings-on-wings

(This poem is a secret.
Keep it close to your chest
or it might stir up a hornets' nest)

Snail's Pace

a snail's face
is not one I'd like to kiss
a snail's pace
goes   something   rather   like   this

a snail's trace…

like

this

The Thicker the Batter the Better

Dropped into the oil to be fried
The fish popped out and cried:

'This thick coat of batter protects me
I've no wish to be rude
but being fried in the nude
would not only embarrass but vex me

Pizza Consultant

Dear Sir,

I wish to apply for the post of pizza topping consultant. As I am very fond of pizzas and enjoy the company of people, I believe I would be most suitable. The job, as I understand it, would be to talk to customers in depth, getting to know their likes and dislikes, dreams and aspirations, background, education, star signs and the like. Using the information, I would then advise them on the topping best suited to their character.

I would be willing either to work in the restaurant itself, or visit the homes of prospective customers who prefer to choose from your extensive take-away menu.

Although unemployed for the last seventeen years, prior to that I was at school.

Yours faithfully

A. Lacey

Jack Pratt

I like my food insipid
Tasteless, mawkish, flat
Vapid, wishy-washy
Yum Yum I like all that

My wife, now she likes spices
Pungent, stinging hot
Peppery, biting, racy
(We don't eat out a lot).

Roll

During the night
while turning over
His stomach
rolled ominously

off the bed.

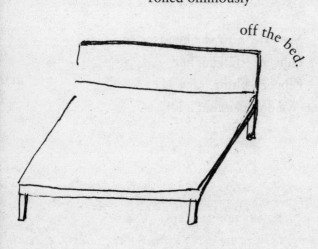

The Burp

One evening at supper
A little girl burped.
'Tut tut,' said mother.
'What do you say?' said father.

Her brother giggled.
'It's not funny,' said father.
'Pardon,' said the little girl.
'That's better,' said mother.

And all was quickly forgotten.
Except, that is, by the burp.
It had only just been born
And already everybody was apologising.

What sort of person gives birth
And then says 'Pardon'?
What sort of relative giggles
Then looks away embarrassed?

Hurt, the baby burp hovered near the ceiling
Looked down at the one who had brought it up
Then escaped through an open window
Never to return.

The Burp II

Like a balloon freed from its skin
the little burp floated high above
the rooftops of London. At the beck
and call of every flick of wind
it toss-tailed over, looped the loop
and zig-zagged down to the Thames.

It was a clear night, and the moon
danced on a tightrope of fairylights
reflected in the black velvety water.
Taking a deep breath, the burp
swooped beneath Battersea Bridge
and across the surface of the river.

Skimming soundlessly through Chelsea
it bobbed through Pimlico and beyond
past the palace at Lambeth, beneath Big Ben
until, on reaching Waterloo, felt its energy
draining away. Soon it would be time.
Gravely, it steered itself towards the shore.

Beneath the arches of the Embankment
figures lay huddled like crumpled litter
and in the flickering shadows against the wall
an old man, more tattered than most, lay sleeping.
What the burp saw was a mouth, wide open
and so was drawn toward it, and entered.

Suddenly the old man's dreams tasted good.
Of sarsaparilla and ice-cream, sponge puddings
aglow with syrup. He gulped them down
those tastes of childhood long since past.
Then snuggling down in his cardboard box
he licked his lips, and breathed his last.

Lucky

There was a boy at school we called 'Lucky'
  All he did was whinge and moan
'Lucky' was the nickname we gave him
  Because he was so accident-prone

If something was spilled or knocked over
  Splattered, burnt or bust
There in the midst of the damage
  Would be Lucky looking nonplussed

He said that bad things happened to him
  Having been born under an unlucky star
And a fortune-teller warned his mother
Not to let him travel far

So to ward off every kind of harm
  The gypsy gave him a lucky charm:
A silver horseshoe, rabbit's paw,
  Lucky heather, eagle's claw,
Coloured glass and polished stones
  Dried hair and yellowing bones

He never walked under ladders
  Never stepped on pavement cracks
Never touched a looking-glass
  Never learned how to relax

You could spot Lucky a mile off
  Count the creases in his frown
As he concentrated on keeping alive
  His pockets weighted down

With a silver horseshoe, rabbit's paw,
  Lucky heather, eagle's claw,
Coloured glass and polished stones
  Dried hair and yellowing bones

Though the streets were full of happy kids
  He was never allowed to play
In case of bombs, or tigers, or ghosts
  So he stayed in, out of harm's way

Then one afternoon his luck changed
  (Friday the Thirteenth, coincidentally)
He'd been kept in detention after school
  For setting fire to it (accidentally)

When hurrying home and touching wood
  For it was then well after dark
Three lads jumped him, mugged him
  Took all he had, near the gates of the park

A silver horseshoe, rabbit's paw,
  Lucky heather, eagle's claw,
Coloured glass and polished stones
  Dried hair and yellowing bones

Lucky lay low and cowered for days
  As if some tragedy would befall
But nothing unusual happened
  Nothing. Simply nothing at all

BANANA SKIN

It was as if he'd been living underwater
  And at last had come up for air
The next week his dad won the lottery
  And became a millionaire

We never saw Lucky after that
  The family moved out to Australia
So the moral is: Chuck them away
  Or doomed you'll be to failure

A silver horseshoe, rabbit's paw,
  Lucky heather, eagle's claw,
Coloured glass and polished stones
  Dried hair and yellowing bones

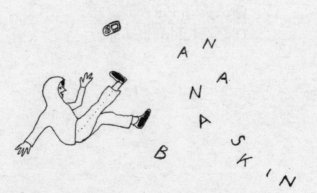

Washed Up

When we were born
We were out of our depth
Now we are all adrift

Adrift, adrift
On a cardboard raft
Now we are all adrift

* * *

When we were young
We were all at sea
Now we are all washed up

Washed up, washed up
On a pavement cold
Old, and all washed up.

Peepshow

The ocean's out there
It's vast and it's home
And I want to be in it
With the freedom to roam

Not stuck in a prison
That's made out of glass
For humans to peer into
As they file past

It's all right for goldfish
And smallfry like that
But I deserve more
Than being ogled at

Imagine the look
You'd have on your face
If you had to live
In such a small space

Little wonder
That I look so glum
Banged up in a seaside
Aquarium.

All in Time to the Music

'All in time, all in time, all in time to the music
All in time, all in time, all in time to the music'...

The sea is outrageous, it rages and rages
All in time to the music
Manacled to the moon for ages and ages
All in time to the music

The sea is secretive, its soul unassailable
All in time to the music
With mountains of water, black and unscalable
All in time to the music

The sea is stricken, terribly sick, an'
All in time to the music
Its arteries thicken, acid and slick, an'
All in time to the music

The sea's in a panic, unstable and manic
All in time to the music
The earth in its clutches, everything touches
All in time to the music

When the earth quakes the devil awakes
All in time to the music
Sends in an army Satanic tsunami
All in time to the music

What begins as a wave becomes a mass grave
All in time to the music
The water recedes, a continent bleeds
All in time to the music

'All in time, all in time, all in time to the music
All in time, all in time, all in time to the music. . .'

Poor Old Dead Horses

Don't give your rocking-horse
To the old rag and bony

He'll go straight to the knacker
And haggle for money

The stirrups are torn off
The bridle and harness

Chopped up for firewood
It is thrown on the furnace

And the water that boils
Is chucked down the sluices

To wash away what remains
Of poor old dead horses.

Borrowed Time

Apparently we are all living
on Borrowed Time.
What I want to know is
Who borrowed it, and from whom?

And another thing...
If we give it back
Can we borrow another?

Shooting Stars

Under cover of daylight they creep up on us
And on cloudy nights close in, slowly but surely

We are surrounded and outnumbered
If it is clear tonight, take a look for yourself

Notice how they keep still while you are watching
Then, as soon as you blink, they have moved

They think you won't notice but you do
The sinister game of statues they are playing

✳ ✳ ✳

That is why I am out here every night
Rifle in hand, picking them off

Trouble is they are fearless. Kill one
And at the speed of light another takes its place

Aliens with all the time in the world
Licking their lips. Twinkling ever closer.

The Magnet

Late autumn, while playing
Near the Abbey ruins, I found
What appeared to be a horseshoe
Half buried in the ground

Or it might have been a doorhandle
Or part of some ancient machine
So I stuck it in my schoolbag
And took it home to clean

It was pitted with rust and covered
With mud and molten tar
But I scrubbed until it shone as bright
As a sheriff's silver star

When, lo and behold, a magnet
That fitted neatly in my palm
And holding it then I felt
A sense of overwhelming calm

With a confidence running through me
That I'd never felt before
Without a word to anyone
I slipped out through the door

Walked down the street and out of town
Along the woodland track
Across the valley and over the hill
Not once did I look back

Holding it out before me
Like a diviner seeking gold
I followed the path to Devil's Crag
By destiny made bold

Drawn toward the darkness
Like a medieval alchemist
Deeper I went into the moor
Where the lolling tongue of the mist

Licked my flesh with an icy coldness
As I stumbled half asleep
The magnet pulling harder now
As if a rendezvous to keep

My partner called a livelier tune
I jigged as in a trance
When a clap of thunder, out of time
Stopped my foolish dance

Destiny took to its heels
And from then on I was frightened
The more I tried to free myself
The more my fingers tightened

Then I tripped. But still the magnet
Dragged me through the gorse
Like an Indian brave whose hands are tied
To a wild runaway horse

The wind on my back was screaming
And digging in its claws
As an eerie power drew me
Across the endless moors

Then a thought came that chilled me
As my strength began to fail
Was it Satan there before me?
Did I have him by the tail?

Straight through the windscreen
Of that nightmare I was thrown
And lay at the foot of Devil's Crag
But no longer alone

A hump-backed beast stood over me
It kicked me in the head
Then snatched the metal from my hand
And left me there for dead

No one believed my story
Though my temple bears the proof
A purple stain that will not fade
In the shape of a cloven hoof.

The Death of Nelson

Lord Nelson, though man as man can be
Suffered from hayfever, even at sea

The French knew this and that is why
They attacked when the pollen count was high

Midst the heat and the dust and the canonsmoke
The allergy struck – he started to choke

In the noonday sun on the Spanish seas
He let go one almighty sneeze

The Battle of Trafalgar Square.

Then sneezed from the fo'c's'le to the stern
(Some folks'll never learn)

His good eye streaming in a wheezing fit
When a musket ball scored a direct hit

I never believed that 'kiss me' stuff
From the lips of an Englishman, heroic and tough

As he sneezed his last he was misheard to say:
'Bless me, Hardy,' then passed away.

Every Little Breeze

Every little breeze
Makes me want to sneeze
When the hay fever season starts in June

When the blossom bursts in May
I'm going far away
Antarctica, or better still, the moon

ASHOOO!

ATISHOO!
SHOO!

Colin

My name is Colin
I'm a pollen
Pollinating is what I do

If you sniff a rose
I'll tickle your nose
Till it glows and goes. . .
Ash-yooo!

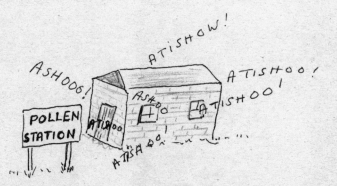

Meet the Cats

I

Allison has allergies
With dizzy spells and wheezes
The sort of puss
Who makes a fuss
Cries: 'There's a man in the room,'
Then sneezes.

II

Marvo, magician extraordinaire
Can juggle and keep seventeen mice in the air
Audiences roar: 'Encore, encore,'
At the sight of this conjuror's sleight-of-paw.

III

There's many a cat in the cats' *Who's Who*
Who rue the cat they once did woo

From Felixstowe to Edinbraw
Titled toms have held her paw

Miaowed her praises, sworn true love
By the light of the milky moon above

Alone now Miranda mopes in her flat
An ex-sex-kitten now a tired old cat.

IV

Thomasina Tittletat
Although a lean
And little cat
Has a tongue as juicy
Long and fat
As a gossip column.

And because of that
Is the uncrowned queen
Of catty chat.

Strangeways

Granny's canary
Escaped from its cage
It's up on the roof
In a terrible rage

Hurling abuse
And making demands
That granny fails
To understand

'Lack of privacy'
'Boring old food'
It holds up placards
Painted and rude

It's not coming down
The canary warns
Till gran carries out
Major reforms.

The message has spread
And now for days
Cage-birds have been acting
In very strange ways.

Multi-Stories

If multi-storey car parks could talk
What stories they could tell
About cars, petrol and parking
But they can't, which is just as well.

If multi-storey car parks could talk
What stories they could tell
About cars, petrol and parking
But they can't, which is just as well.

If multi-storey car parks could talk
What stories they could tell
About cars, petrol and parking
But they can't, which is just as well.

Rhyming in Court

The Rhyming Accused:

'Have mercy m'lud, and I'll try to be good
Think twice before breaking the law.
Drop the case, put a smile on my face
And you'll never see me no more.'

The Rhyming Judge:

'Young man, I don't like your attitude
I find you cheeky, rather rude
And today I'm in a very bad mood.

So I've just one more thing to say
Before the uniforms drag you away...
Eighteen months. Have a nice day.'

Cobblers

'Footing the Bill'
is the name of the shop
that repairs the boots
of the British cop.

So You Want to be a Letter?

If you want to be a letter of the Alphabet,
better not choose *D*.

Of course, you could be a *deer* or a *darling*
a *diamond* or a *daffodil*, even a *dictionary*
But you're more likely to end up in *debt*,
dead and *decomposing*. A *dumbstruck dunce*,
dirty, disruptive, depressed and *disadvantaged*.
A *disgusting dork*.

If I were you, I'd choose *A*.
An amazing angel astride an adorable aardvaark,
for instance.

Crocodile Farm

Come wi' me
Down to Crocodile Farm
If you keep your eyes open
You'll come to no harm

There's the old milking shed
Where it's all done by hand
Though we've lost quite a few
As you'll well understand

We make crocodile butter
Yoghurt and cream
Though nobody buys it
It's all lumpy and green

High up on the pastures
They're put out to graze
Where they round up the shepherds
And worry them for days

Then we fatten them up
And kill them humanely
The ones we can catch –
They kill us, mainly

But crocodile meat
Is an acquired taste
A cross between sewage
And stale salmon paste

So I'm giving up crocodiles
Cos my account's in the red
And starting a farm
For alligators instead.

Everything Touches

Everything touches, life interweaves
Starlight and wood-smoke, ashes and leaves
Birdsong and thunder, acid and rain
Everything touches, unbroken chain

Rainstorm and rainbow, warrior and priest
Stingray and dolphin, beauty and beast
Heartbeat and high tide, ebb tide and flow
The universe in a crystal of snow

Snowdrop and death-cap, hangman and clown
Walls that divide come tumbling down
Seen through the night, the glimmer of day
Light is but darkness worn away

Blackness and whiteness, sunset and dawn
Those gone before, yet to be born
Past and future, distance and time
Atom to atom, water to wine

Look all around and what do you see?
Everything touches, you're touching me
Look all around and what do you see?
Everything touches, you're touching me.

Morning Has Broken

Morning has broken. . .
Is it too late to mend it?

Too late the billion gallons of sun cream
Smeared over the earth's burning body
The straw hat covering three continents
Too late the giant parasol
The sunglasses wrapped around the equator
Too late the ozone elastoplast

Morning has broken. . .
Is it too late to mend it?

Keep Your Eyes Peeled

In my field of vision
In that watery field
Grow potatoes with eyes in
Which is why I keep them peeled.

Trying to Write

Trying to write without a rhyme	a
Gets more difficult all the time	a
I wish that I could now reverse	b
This facility in me verse.	b

How to Get Published

Dear Sir or Madam
I wish to apply
For the post of
Poetry Editor

On your magazine.
I have been writing
Verse for many years
So far without suc-

cess. The position
Therefore would give me
A wonderful opp-
ortunity to

See myself in print.
I look forward to
An early reply.
Yours faithfully etc.

Sylvia Tendril

Sing Their Praises Loud

The Earl of Sandwich invented the sandwich
Or rather, gave it a name
The Duke of Wellington invented the wellie
(Not his only claim to fame)

Lord Gladstone gave us the gladstone bag
Lord Fountain the fountain pen
So many amazing inventions
So many inventive, upper-class men

But who can remember Emily Frying
(Forgotten, not being a man)
For she it was who invented
The household frying pan?

And what about Hilary Teapot?
And her cousin Charlotte Garden-Hose?
Norah Napkin? Cordelia Catflap?
The list simply grows and grows

Susanna Shoehorn, Caroline Inkwell
Daisy Thimble, Jennifer Toothpick
Isabel Tweezers, Delia Dentalfloss
June Spitoon, Francoise Cul-de-Sac

Indira Pashmina, Betty Birthbath
Mary-Lou Cufflink, Victoria Gusset
Agatha Bookmark, Shirley Hairspray
Maureen Rucksack, Ella May Forklift-Truck

So many inspiring women
Of whom we should all be proud
Add your own names to the list
And sing their praises loud . . .

Beguiling

She is so beguiling
That when she beckons
I can run a mile in
Twenty seconds.

A Poem About That

I am walking down the street
Thinking about life and beauty
And football and TV and about
What to have for supper
When he stops me and says
'Cheer up, it might never happen.'

But it already has
Because then he says 'How are you?'
And proceeds to tell me about how he is
And about how he was
And about how he will be
And about
And about
And about
And about
And about
And about
And about
And about an hour later he says
'I bet you could write a poem about that.'

The Book Borrower

Seeing it on the shelf
    or by the chair
She seizes it
    and settles down

Ignores my cold stare
    my worried frown
Feels not the rising
    of my hackles

She is immersed
    so deeply
the page crackles

I know what's coming next
    have seen it all before
The novel begun
    is about to become
the novel half read

'Book Borrowers Anonymous'
    I whisper as she makes for the door
She turns: 'Can I borrow it
    until the weekend?'

Never lend, I tell myself
    Never lend. But I weaken
Say 'Of course' and watch her go

I never learn
    I should be firm. Say 'No'
But I haven't the knack

I should give her
    a piece of my mind
But I'd never get it back.

The dAdA Christmas Catalogue

chocolate co**M**b

Can-*of*-w**Or**ms OPENer

One b**O**ok **E**nd

Solar-**poWer**ed *sun*-bed

*Abrasi*ve *partrid*Ges

Inflatable *fridge*

Set *of* **nervous** door handles

Overnight tea-bag

Instant cof**fe**e table

Sly tromb**one**

Pair of *cheap*skat**es**

MObile phone-**booth**

Underwater ash**tray**

13 *amp* bath **plug**

Pair **of socks, identical** but for the colour

Another *book* END

Port**able suitcase**

Genetic **make-up** bag

De**my**stifying *spray*

Packet of pARTy-*poopers*

Nasal fl0Ss *(unwaxed)*

Con**tact** *lens* **adhesive**

maGnetic chopsticks

Concrete poetry-**mixer**

Non-secat**eurs**

Not a Pipe.

Christmastide

When the Christmas tide comes in
May it bring a shoal of gifts
To surprise and delight.

When the Christmas tide goes out
May the shore be strewn
With happy memories.

(But no litter please)

Almost a Riddle

I'm a good friend but you couldn't care less
Rub my face in it as I clean up your mess

Toss me aside but I'll bounce back
At leaving no traces I've learned the knack

You ignore me when things go well
But seek me out when you mis-spell

(Oops! You've given the game away)
If you'd written this in pencil I might have saved the day.

Riddle

I'm older than my eldest son
But younger than my mother
One ear has an eagle tattooed on
Skull and crossbones on the other
What am I?

The Outlaw's In-laws

An outlaw's mother
And mother-in-law
Went riding down
In Witchita

The latter, without
A trace of remorse
Pushed the former
Off her horse

Now the outlaw's mother
Is stiff as a board
And the outlaw's mother-
in-law, outlawed.

What Is It?

I walked down the lane and then I saw it
Turned into a field and there it was

I climbed up the hill and then I saw it
Scrambled down the other side and there it was

I dashed across the bridge and then I saw it
Reached the river bank and there it was

I ran towards the house and then I saw it
Hurried up the garden path and there it was

I collapsed into a chair and then I saw it
Closed my eyes, fell asleep and there it was.

The Figment Tree

I believe in fairies
And each Sunday after tea
At the bottom of the garden
Beneath the figment tree
Alone, I sit and wonder
If they believe in me.

On and on...

Is a well-wisher
    someone
who wishes at a well?

Is a bad speller
    one
who casts a wicked spell?

ABRER
CODABRA!

Is a shop-lifter
    a giant
who goes around lifting shops?

Is a popsinger
    someone
who sings and then pops?

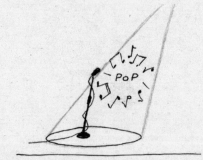

Is a fly fisherman
    an angler
who fishes for flies?

Is an eye-opener
    a gadget
for opening eyes?

Is a night nurse
    a nurse
who looks after the night?

Who puts it to bed
    and then
turns off the light?

Is a pot-holer
    a gunman
who shoots holes in pots?

Does a baby-sitter
    really
sit on tiny tots?

Is a big spender
    a spendthrift
who is exceedingly big?

Is a pig farmer
    really
a land-owning pig?

...and on...

Is a blood donor
    pitta bread
stuffed with blood?

Is a tree surgeon
    a doctor
made out of wood?

Is a monster crane
    a ferocious
man-eating crane?

Is a train-spotter
    an artist
        who paints spots on a train?

Is an all-rounder
    an athlete
who is completely round?

Is a sound engineer
    one
who is completely sound?

Is a cardsharper
    a craftsman
who sharpens cards?

Who guards women
    when
a guardsman guards?

Is a batsman
    a man
who is completely bats?

Is a cat burglar
    a thief
who likes stealing cats?

Is a flat tyre
    a tyre
that you keep in a flat?

Is a hat-trick
    a method
of stealing a hat?

...and on...

Is a rain hood
    a gangster
who sings in the rain?

Will a pain-killer
    kill you
in terrible pain?

Is a tail-gunner
a gunner
with a big long tail?

Do shoppers buy
giants
in a giant sale?

Does a lightning conductor
conduct
orchestras fast?

Is a past master
a master
who has mastered the past?

Is a light bulb
   a bulb
that is light as a feather?

Does an opera buff
   sing
in the altogether

Is a fire bucket
   a bucket
that bursts into flames?

Is a gamesmanship
   where sailors
go to play games?

Is a dinner-lady
    what cannibals
eat for their dinner?

If you eat your words
    will you
grow thinner?

WORD BURGER

...and on...

Is a slip road
a road
that is covered in ice?

Are price cuts
wounds
you get at a price?

Is a waiting room
    a room
that patiently waits?

Is a gate-keeper's
    hobby
collecting gates?

Is a prayer mat
    a carpet
that sings hymns and prays?

Is a horsefly
    a fly
that gallops and neighs?

Does a pony trap
    trap ponies
going to the fair?

Is fire-hose
    stockings
that firemen wear?

Is witchcraft
    jewellery
made by a witch?

Does a battery hen
    cry
when you turn the switch?

When a bricklayer
    lays a brick
what hatches?

Is a scratch team
    so itchy
it scratches?

...and on.

Is sandpaper
    used
for wrapping up sand?

If you lay down
    your arms
can you still lend a hand?

Is a sick bed
    a bed
that is feeling unwell?

Is a crime wave
    a criminal's
wave of farewell?

Is a cop shop
　a shop
where you can purchase a cop?

Is the last laugh
　the long one
before the big drop?

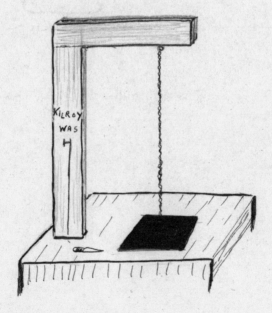

Is a bent copper
    a policeman
who has gone round the bend?

Is the bottom line
    the line
on your bottom?

the end

Roger McGough is one of Britain's
best-loved poets, who also writes for the stage
and television. He has been awarded an OBE and
a CBE for services to poetry, and was recently
honoured with The Freedom of the City of Liverpool.
His many books for children include *Slapstick*,
All the Best, *Bad, Bad Cats*, and for Frances Lincoln,
Dotty Inventions, *Until I Met Dudley* and
An Imaginary Menagerie.
Called "the patron saint of poetry" by the poet laureate
Carol Ann Duffy, Roger McGough gives readings
and performances all over the world.
He lives in London.

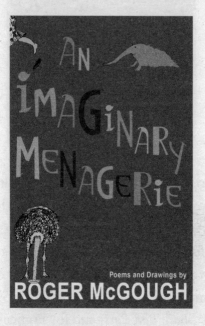

978-1-84780-269-9 • PB • £5.99

Funny, fantastic, outrageous, wise...
a powerful mix of comic and serious verse
from one of the UK's most popular poets.

"Wild and witty" – *Telegraph*

978-1-84780-167-8 • PB • £5.99

With wordplay and riddles, and poems that will make you laugh, tell you stories and make you think, this is a brilliant debut from an exciting new poet.

"A box of delights" – *Carol Ann Duffy*

978-1-84780-169-2 • PB • £5.99

From spooky legends to dreamy poems, teasers and rhymes, expect the unexpected. A poetry adventure waiting to happen!

"A poet with a powerful feeling for story and language" – *Carousel*